# THE HIDDEN MESSAGE

Written by
DAVID BOYD

Illustrated by
JEFF ALWARD

This story is set in Elizabethan England. Each chapter ends with a non-fiction page that gives more information about real people's lives and actual events at that time.

OXFORD
UNIVERSITY PRESS

WILLIAM SHAKESPEARE

KIT MARLOWE

RICHARD BURBAGE

FRANCIS WALSINGHAM

ELIZABETH I

JASPER KYD

## REAL PEOPLE IN HISTORY

**WILLIAM (WILL) SHAKESPEARE (1564–1616)** became the greatest English writer and poet of all time.

**CHRISTOPHER (KIT) MARLOWE (1564–1593)** became a well-known poet and playwright.

**RICHARD BURBAGE (1567–1619)** was a famous Elizabethan actor. His father, James Burbage, was a friend of Shakespeare's.

**FRANCIS WALSINGHAM (1530–1590)** was head of the Queen's spy network.

**ELIZABETH I (1533–1603)** was Queen of England.

## FICTIONAL CHARACTER

**JASPER KYD** is a child actor in this story.

# Contents

Queen Elizabeth I

This story takes place in the reign of Queen Elizabeth I. She was Queen of England from 1558 to 1603. Her long reign is known as the Elizabethan Age.

| 1533 >> | 1558 >> | 1564 >> | 1571 >> | 1586 >> |
|---|---|---|---|---|
| Elizabeth is born at Greenwich Palace. | Elizabeth becomes Queen of England. | William Shakespeare and Christopher Marlowe are born in the same year. | Elizabeth names Francis Walsingham chief spymaster. | The supporters of Mary, Queen of Scots plan to remove Elizabeth from the throne. |

# ENGLAND

This was a remarkable time in the history of England. England was a rich and powerful country. English explorers sailed to many places to discover new lands.

William Shakespeare

London was the centre of art and literature. Shakespeare and other playwrights wrote some of the best works of English poetry and literature during this period. Plays were very popular, and the theatre was a favourite form of entertainment.

Queen Elizabeth had spies to protect her from her enemies. She died at the age of 70.

Theatre masks

This story is set in an actual time in history, although some of the events are fictional. Real events during this period are shown on the timeline below.

| 1587 » | 1588 » | 1593 » | 1603 » | 1616 » |
|---|---|---|---|---|
| Mary, Queen of Scots is put to death. | Philip II of Spain attacks England and is defeated. | Christopher Marlowe dies. | Queen Elizabeth I dies. James I becomes King of England. | William Shakespeare dies. |

# THE GLOBE THEATRE

The new Globe Theatre

The Globe Theatre was built in 1598. It stood on the bank of the River Thames in London. Many of Shakespeare's plays were performed in this theatre.

The Globe Theatre was octagonal (eight-sided) in shape and opened to the sky in the centre. It could seat up to 3,000 people.

The stage was roughly a quarter of the size of a netball court. It had trapdoors in its floor and ropes overhead for stage work. There was no way to light the stage at night, so plays were performed only in the afternoon.

The Globe Theatre burned down in 1613 when a cannon set the roof on fire. The theatre was rebuilt almost immediately. It was torn down in 1644 to make room for houses.

In 1997, a new Globe Theatre was built near the site of the old one. The building and the stage were designed to be as close to the original as possible. In its first year, the new Globe drew an audience of nearly a quarter of a million people.

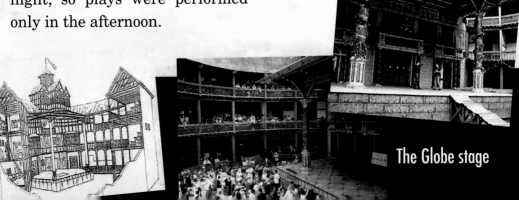

The Globe stage

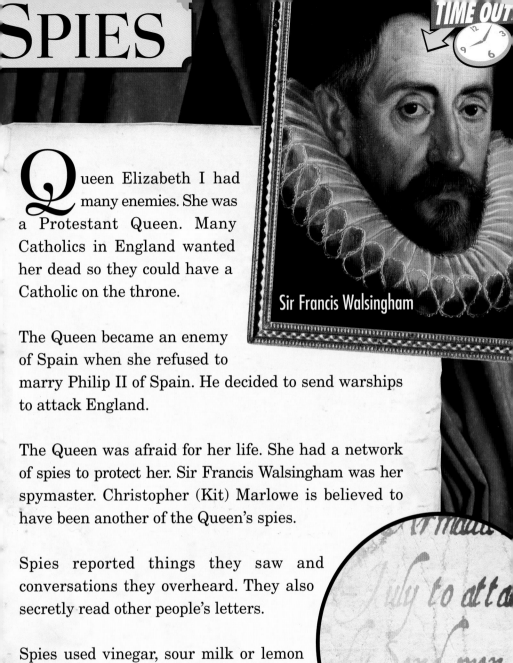

# SPIES

Sir Francis Walsingham

Queen Elizabeth I had many enemies. She was a Protestant Queen. Many Catholics in England wanted her dead so they could have a Catholic on the throne.

The Queen became an enemy of Spain when she refused to marry Philip II of Spain. He decided to send warships to attack England.

The Queen was afraid for her life. She had a network of spies to protect her. Sir Francis Walsingham was her spymaster. Christopher (Kit) Marlowe is believed to have been another of the Queen's spies.

Spies reported things they saw and conversations they overheard. They also secretly read other people's letters.

Spies used vinegar, sour milk or lemon juice to write secret messages. These secret messages could be read when the paper was carefully heated over a candle flame.

# MARLOWE'S DEATH

Christopher
Marlowe

Christopher Marlowe was a friend of Shakespeare's and a talented writer. Like Shakespeare, he wrote many plays for the theatre.

Marlowe died when he was only 29. Who killed him? Why? There are many questions around the death of Marlowe. Records that might tell us more either never existed or were destroyed over the years. His death remains a mystery today.

BACK AT SHAKESPEARE'S ...

WILL, WE HAVE TERRIBLE NEWS.

WHAT IS IT?

KIT MARLOWE HAS BEEN KILLED!

THE NEWS SHOCKS SHAKESPEARE.

KIT? WHY? HOW?

AN ARGUMENT OVER THE BILL. HE WAS STABBED.

KIT WAS IN THIS VERY ROOM THIS MORNING! HE TOOK ONE OF MY SONNETS. I WISH I COULD TELL HIM NOW THAT I DIDN'T MIND.

SHAKESPEARE'S WARM HEART TAKES OVER.

... AND THEN YOU SAW THAT I HAD WRITTEN A FRESH COPY OF THE SONNET. THE ORIGINAL WAS NO LONGER NEEDED.

YES. BUT MR BURBAGE AND RICHARD SAW ME. PLEASE LET ME PLAY MERCUTIO! PLEASE DON'T TAKE THAT AWAY FROM ME!

WILL, DO WHAT YOU WANT WITH JASPER. FIRE HIM IF YOU WISH. I WON'T OBJECT.

I'VE BEEN CALLED TO DEPTFORD TO IDENTIFY POOR MARLOWE'S BODY AND TO TAKE CARE OF HIS BURIAL.

WE'LL ALL MEET TOMORROW NIGHT TO REMEMBER HIM.

WE WILL INDEED!

NO. NO, IT DOESN'T. THIS IS JUST SOME TRICK OF HIS. KIT MARLOWE COULD NEVER BE A SPY!

I COULDN'T STAND IT IF IT WAS MY FAULT.

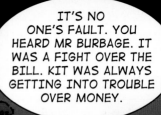

IT'S NO ONE'S FAULT. YOU HEARD MR BURBAGE. IT WAS A FIGHT OVER THE BILL. KIT WAS ALWAYS GETTING INTO TROUBLE OVER MONEY.

JASPER, TOMORROW I WANT YOU TO GO TO THE BANK ON LONDON BRIDGE. DEPOSIT THESE PLAYS AND THIS SONNET FOR ME.

NOW, SLEEP WELL ... OR AS WELL AS YOU CAN. GOD SAVE THE QUEEN!

GOOD NIGHT, SIR. *GOD SAVE THE QUEEN!*

AND GOD SAVE POOR KIT MARLOWE ...

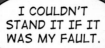

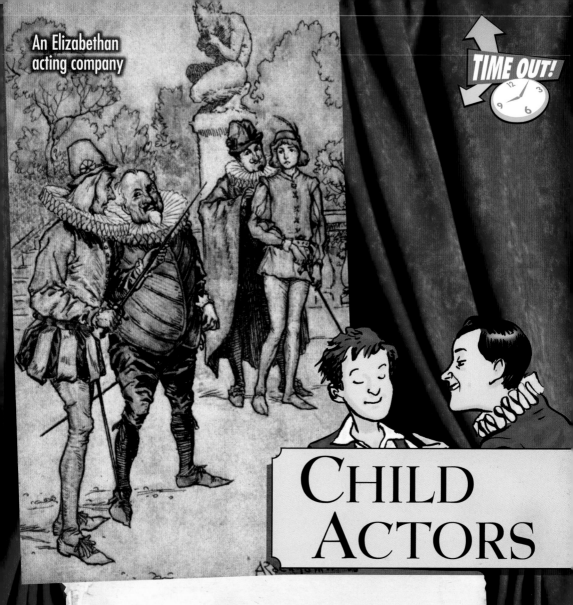

An Elizabethan acting company

# CHILD ACTORS

In Shakespeare's theatre, there were 26 actors. Ten of them were boys. The rest were men. There were no female actors.

People did not approve of female actors, so women's roles were played by boys. Child actors regularly performed in theatres in Elizabethan England.

A strict religious group, called the Puritans, was strongly opposed to the theatre. In 1642, they forced theatres to close for more than 10 years. By the time the theatres reopened, there were no boys trained for the stage. So women took on the female roles. However, it was many years before people approved of female actors.

# CHAPTER 5: Not a Traitor!

YOU ARE KIND TO SAY THAT. BUT I HAVEN'T COME ABOUT THE SONNET.

YOU HAVEN'T?

NO, SIR, I HAVE NOT. I WISH TO SPEAK OF THE DEATH OF CHRISTOPHER MARLOWE. I'M CERTAIN THAT YOU'VE HEARD OF IT.

YES. ALL BECAUSE OF A FIGHT OVER A BILL.

FORGIVE ME, SIR, BUT NEITHER OF US BELIEVES THAT STORY. LET'S BE OPEN WITH EACH OTHER.

A HARSH LAUGH BURSTS FORTH OUT OF A DARK CORNER.

HAHAHA...

HE'S GOT YOU THERE, WALSINGHAM.

YOUR MAJESTY!

RISE.

41

YES, I AM OLD, MASTER POET. I CAN SEE IT IN YOUR EYES. YOU'RE WONDERING JUST HOW OLD YOUR QUEEN IS.

YOUR MAJESTY, IF I MAY ...

SHAKESPEARE RECITES SEVERAL LINES FROM HIS SONNET SO THAT THE QUEEN WILL KNOW OF HIS LOVE AND RESPECT FOR HER.

SO LONG AS MEN CAN BREATHE, OR EYES CAN SEE, SO LONG LIVES THIS, AND THIS GIVES LIFE TO THEE.

YOU HAVE A QUICK MIND AND AN HONEST JUDGEMENT. BUT LET'S GET TO THE POINT. YOU'RE HERE ABOUT KIT MARLOWE.

IT'S FAIR TO SAY, YOUR MAJESTY, THAT HE DIED IN SERVICE TO YOU.

HE WAS A TRAITOR! HE BETRAYED HIS COUNTRY TO THE SPANISH AND DIED A TRAITOR'S DEATH FOR IT.

SO YOU SAY. HOW DO YOU EXPLAIN THIS NOTE, THEN?

WHERE DID YOU GET THIS? HOW DO YOU KNOW ABOUT THIS?

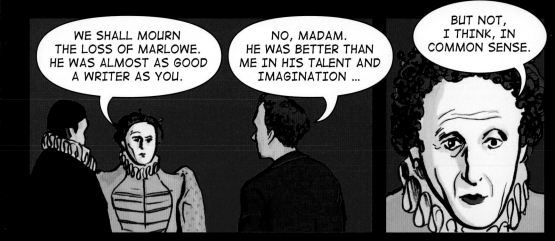

WE SHALL MOURN THE LOSS OF MARLOWE. HE WAS ALMOST AS GOOD A WRITER AS YOU.

NO, MADAM. HE WAS BETTER THAN ME IN HIS TALENT AND IMAGINATION ...

BUT NOT, I THINK, IN COMMON SENSE.

AS HE GOES OUT INTO THE SUNLIGHT, SHAKESPEARE WRITES THE LAST WORDS ABOUT HIS FRIEND ...

'COWARDS DIE MANY TIMES BEFORE THEIR DEATHS; THE VALIANT NEVER TASTE OF DEATH BUT ONCE'.

LONDON IS CALLING. SHAKESPEARE IS NEEDED AT THE THEATRE. AFTER ALL, THERE IS A NEW MERCUTIO TO TRAIN ... AND THE SUDDEN, HORRIBLE THOUGHT OF JASPER KYD LEAPING AROUND WITH A SWORD ON STAGE QUICKENS SHAKESPEARE'S STEPS ...

# SHAKESPEARE'S PLAYS

MR. WILLIAM
SHAKESPEARES
COMEDIES,
HISTORIES, &
TRAGEDIES.
Published according to the True Originall Copies.

LONDON
Printed by Isaac Iaggard, and Ed. Blount. 1623.

Shakespeare's plays are among the best ever written. In all, there are 37 plays that bear his name. Some examples are *Romeo and Juliet*, *Julius Caesar* and *Hamlet*.

Only a few of Shakespeare's plays were published during his lifetime. Most were not printed until after his death. In 1623, several of Shakespeare's close friends collected all his plays and published them.

Shakespeare also wrote 154 sonnets. Many were beautiful love poems that people still read today.

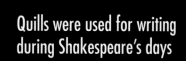

Quills were used for writing during Shakespeare's days

MOVING ON

# LIFE IN ELIZABETHAN ENGLAND

There was no Internet, television or video games, so what did people do for entertainment? You'll be surprised!

English people during the Elizabethan Age worked hard, but they also played hard. Music was a big part of their lives. Wealthy families hired musicians to play music during their meals. The poor sang at work or enjoyed free public concerts. The fiddle, bagpipe, flute and recorder were popular musical instruments.

Dancing was a popular pastime. And everyone enjoyed the theatre. Puppeteers and acrobats were also popular.

Elizabethan men and women spent a lot of time on their hair. Men wore their hair shoulder length or put on wigs to look fashionable. Women dyed their hair and wore hair nets, jewels, pins and hair combs.

Elizabethan fashion was influenced by the Spanish and French styles. Women wore tight-fitting gowns with big ruffle collars. Men wore silk stockings and leather shoes with cloaks and wide hats.

We are all familiar with Elizabethan fashion and costumes because Shakespeare's plays are still very popular today. And movies of Shakespeare's plays are box-office hits!

From the movie
*Shakespeare in Love*

# INDEX

# GLOSSARY

**admit** – to own up to something, sometimes reluctantly

**confess** – to state openly that you have done something wrong

**loyal** – to firmly support someone

**Mercutio (mer-q-she-o)** – a character in Shakespeare's play *Romeo and Juliet*

**original** – the first one of something, not a copy

**self-defence** – the act of defending yourself

**sonnet** – a kind of poem with 14 lines

**spy** – someone who works secretly to find out things

**traitor** – someone who betrays his or her country or friends, by helping the enemy